CREATIVE COLOURING FOR GROWN-UPS

THE CLASSIC COMIC COLOURING BOOK

Michael O'Mara Books Limited

First published in Great Britain in 2015 by
Michael O'Mara Books Limited
9 Lion Yard
Tremadoc Road
London SW4 7NQ

A CIP catalogue record for this book is available from the British Library.

Papers used by Michael O'Mara Books Limited are natural, recyclable products
made from wood grown in sustainable forests. The manufacturing processes
conform to the environmental regulations of the country of origin.

We have made our best efforts to ensure that the artworks reproduced herein are
all in the public domain. We apologize for any errors, which will be corrected in
future editions.

ISBN: 978-1-78243-409-2

3 4 5 6 7 8 9 10

www.mombooks.com

Designed by Claire Cater

Printed and bound in Spain

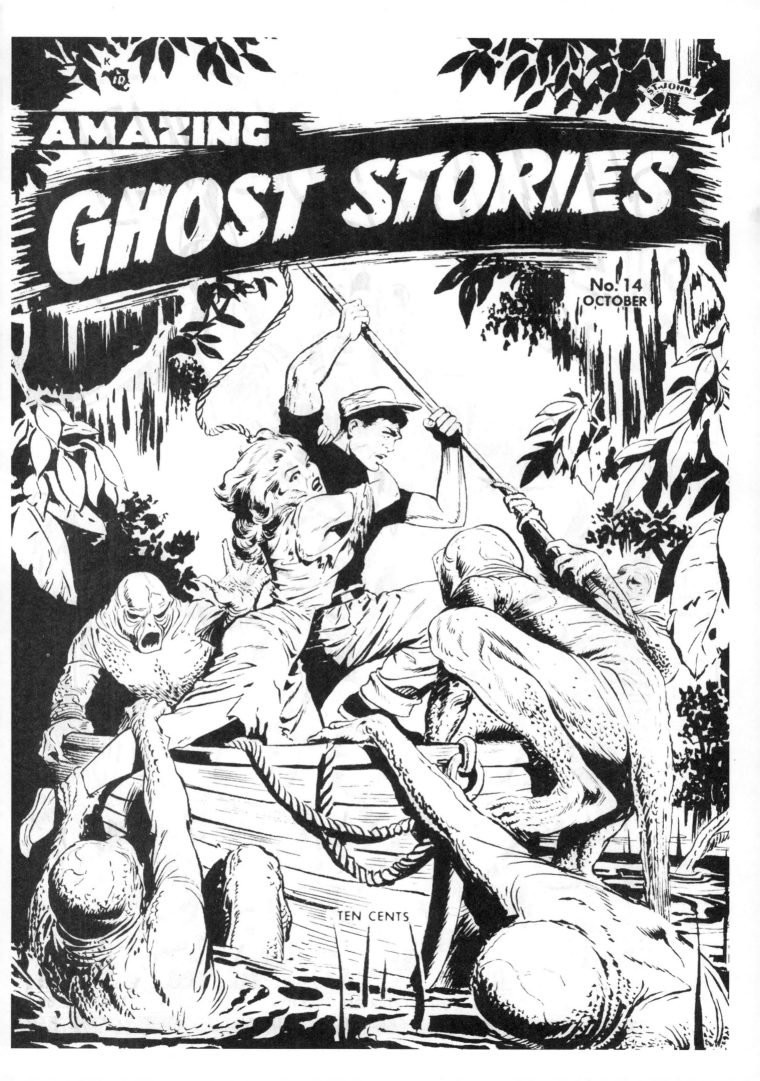

ALL ORIGINAL!!! ALL NEW!!! ALL COMPLETE!!!
BRENDA STARR
NO. 9
JULY
SUPERIOR COMIC
1949
10¢
AUTHORIZED A. C. M. P.
CONFORMS to the COMICS CODE

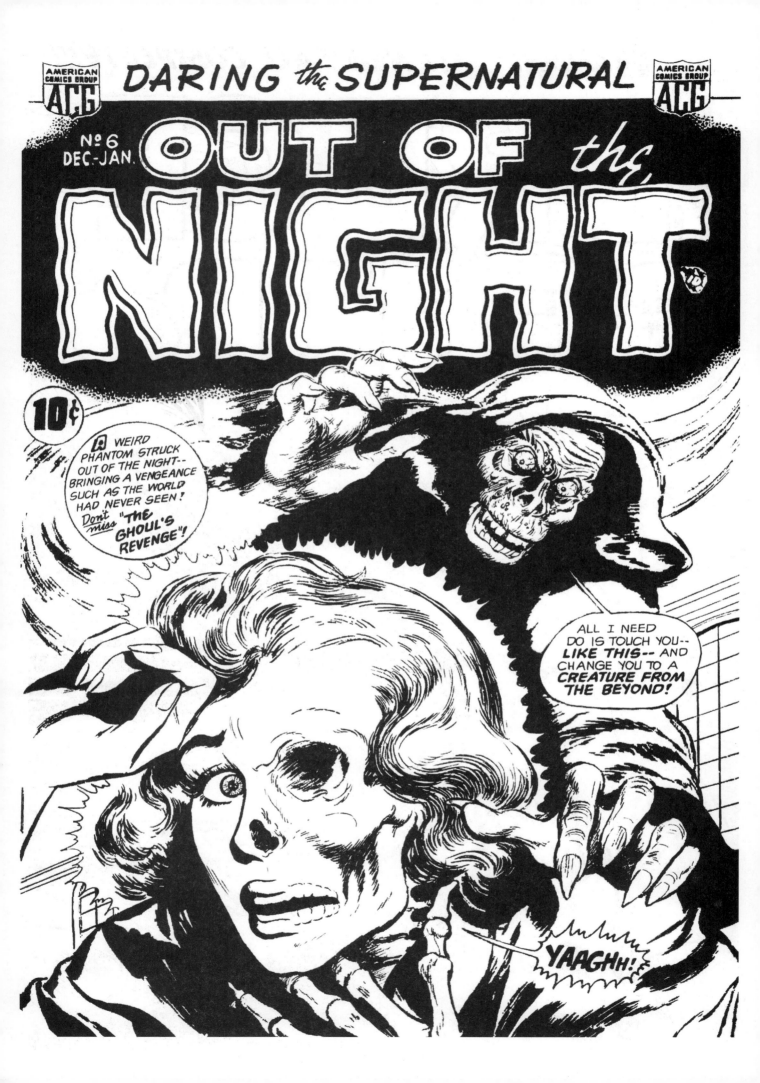

ALL ORIGINAL!!! ALL NEW!!! ALL COMPLETE!!!
No. 5
APRIL
SUPERIOR COMIC
ANC
BRUCE GENTRY
10c

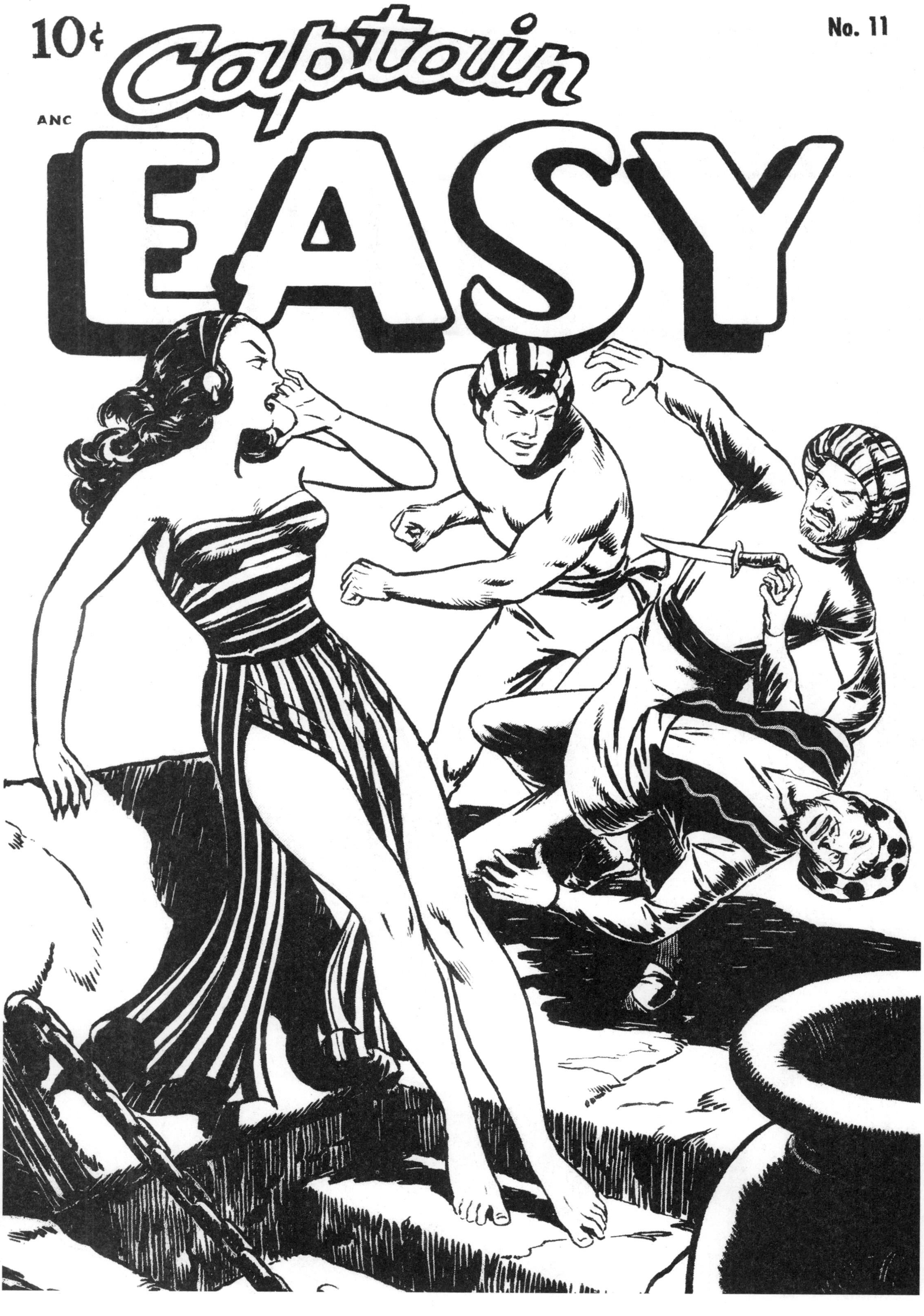
10¢
Captain
ANC
EASY
No. 11

DETECTIVE EYE

No. 2 DEC. 10c
(15c in Canada)

JACK BARRISTER
with the help of
THE EYE
fights a fierce
BATTLE
on the Ocean floor
•
The **AIRMAN**,
with wings spread,
And ROCKET
BLASTING,
escapes
a fate
Worse Than
DEATH
•
Also —
**Don Rance and
the MYSTICAPE**
•
Ken TRAYMORE
•
PACK MORGAN
•
*10 Exciting
Features*

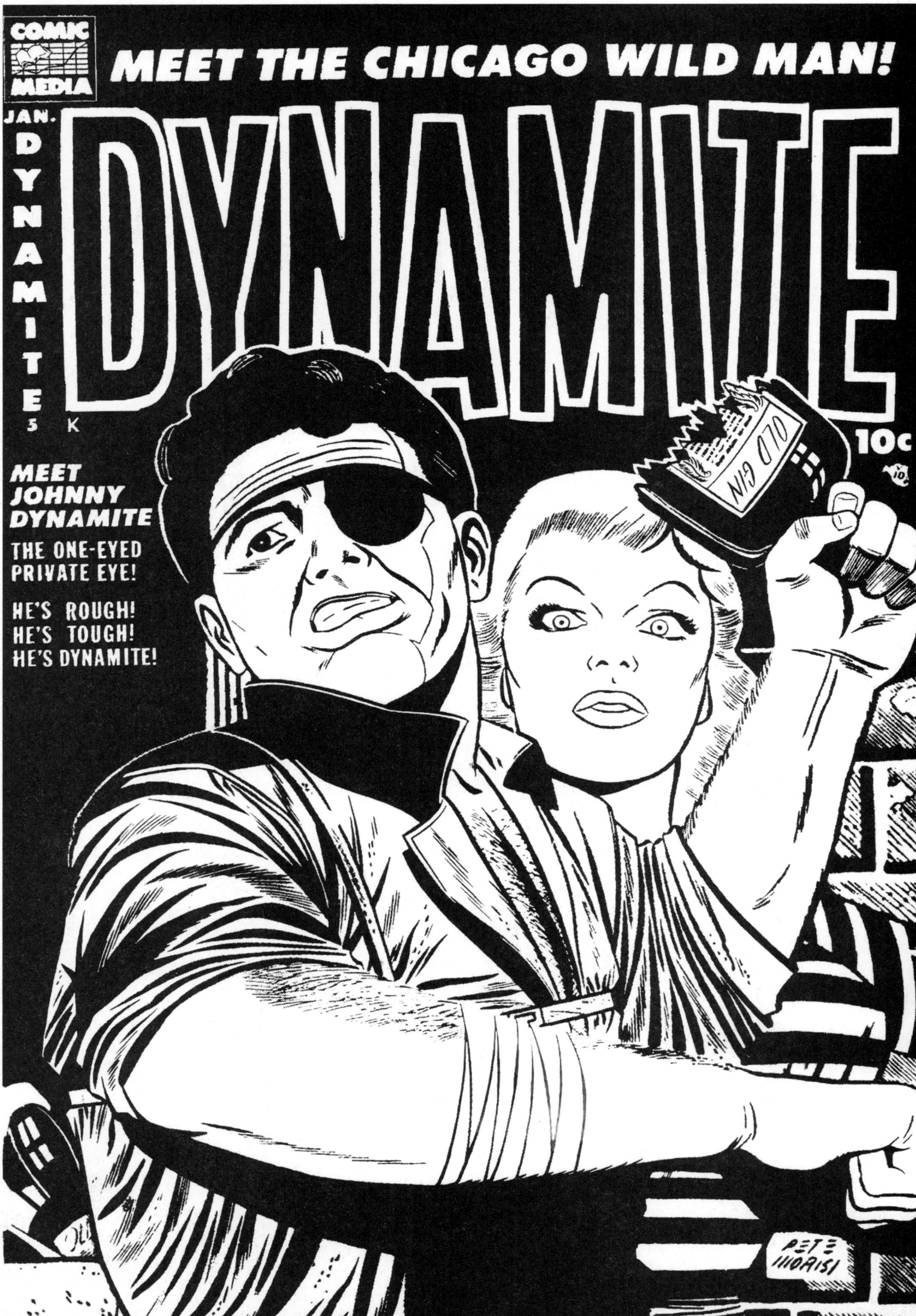
COMIC MEDIA
MEET THE CHICAGO WILD MAN!
JAN.
DYNAMITE
DYNAMITE
5 K
10c
OLD GIN
MEET JOHNNY DYNAMITE
THE ONE-EYED PRIVATE EYE!
HE'S ROUGH! HE'S TOUGH! HE'S DYNAMITE!
PETE MORISI

FDC
DON FORTUNE
MAGAZINE
DEC.
No. 5
10¢
DELECTA OF THE PLANETS!
DON FORTUNE IN THRILL-PACKED ACTION!
LOTS OF LAUGH FEATURES!

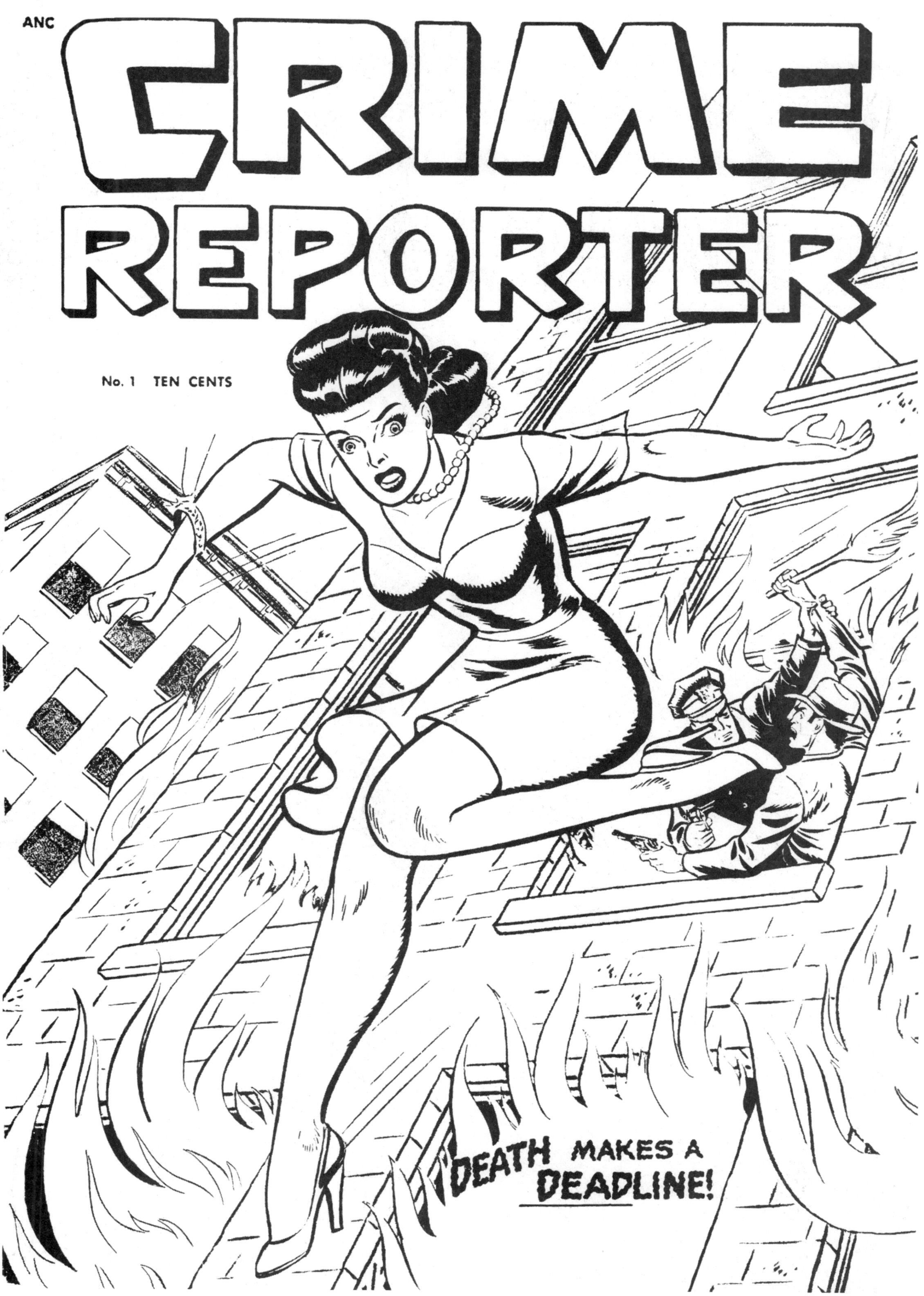
ANC
CRIME REPORTER
No. 1 TEN CENTS
DEATH MAKES A DEADLINE!

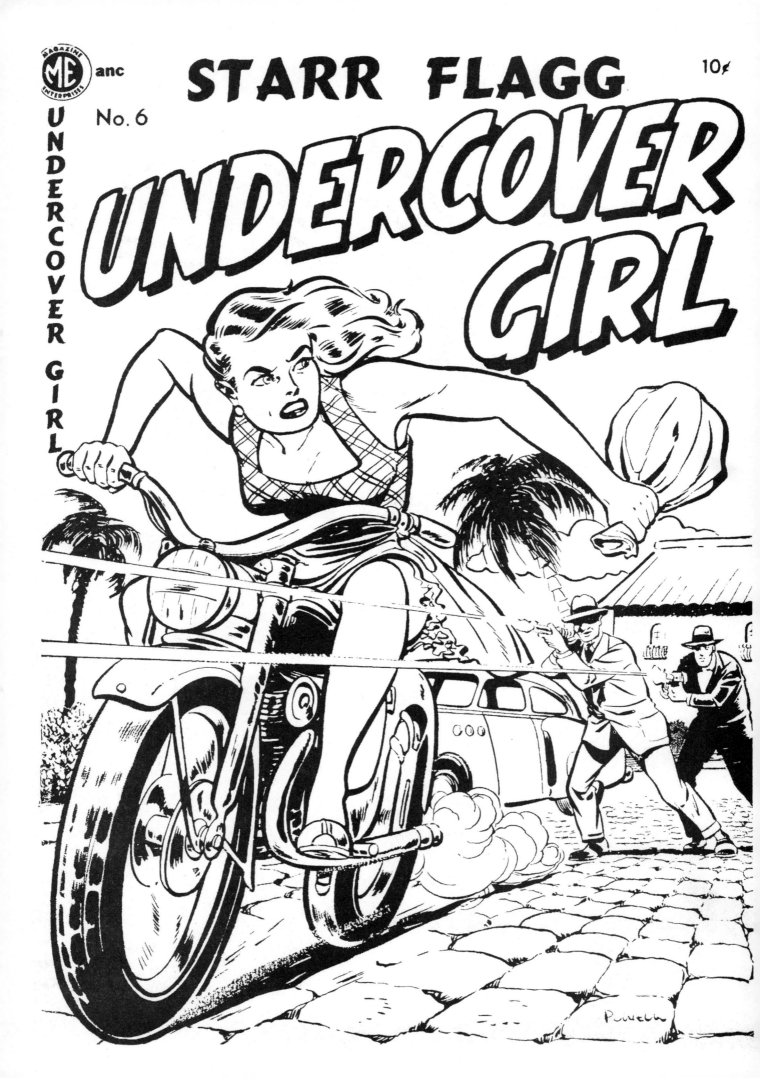

A.N.C.

COWGIRL
Romances

No. 7
10¢

FICTION HOUSE MAGAZINES 30th YEAR!

COWGIRL ROMANCES

"NOBODY LOVES A GUN MAN"

"THE RANGE of TWISTED BRANDS"

AND OTHER THRILLING WESTERN ROMANCES!

STANDARD COMICS
TERROR THAT STALKS BY NIGHT!
ANC
THE UNSEEN
No. 7
10c
TIME IS THE KILLER

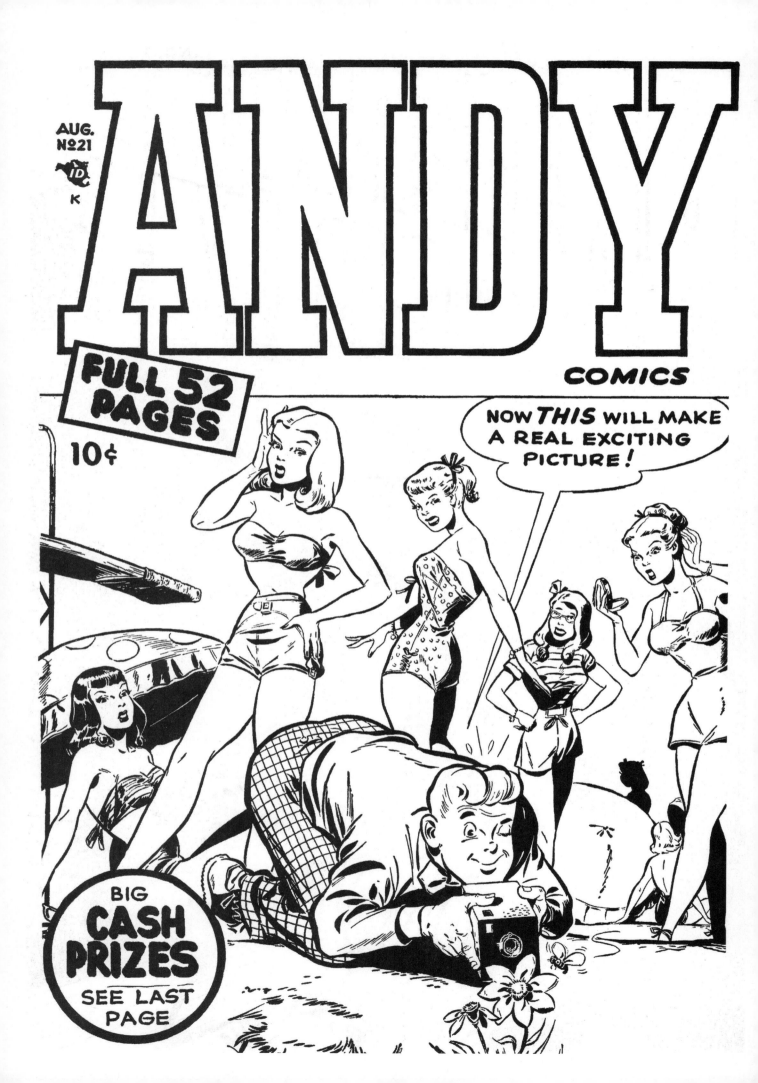

NO. 7

UNDERWORLD CRIME

10¢

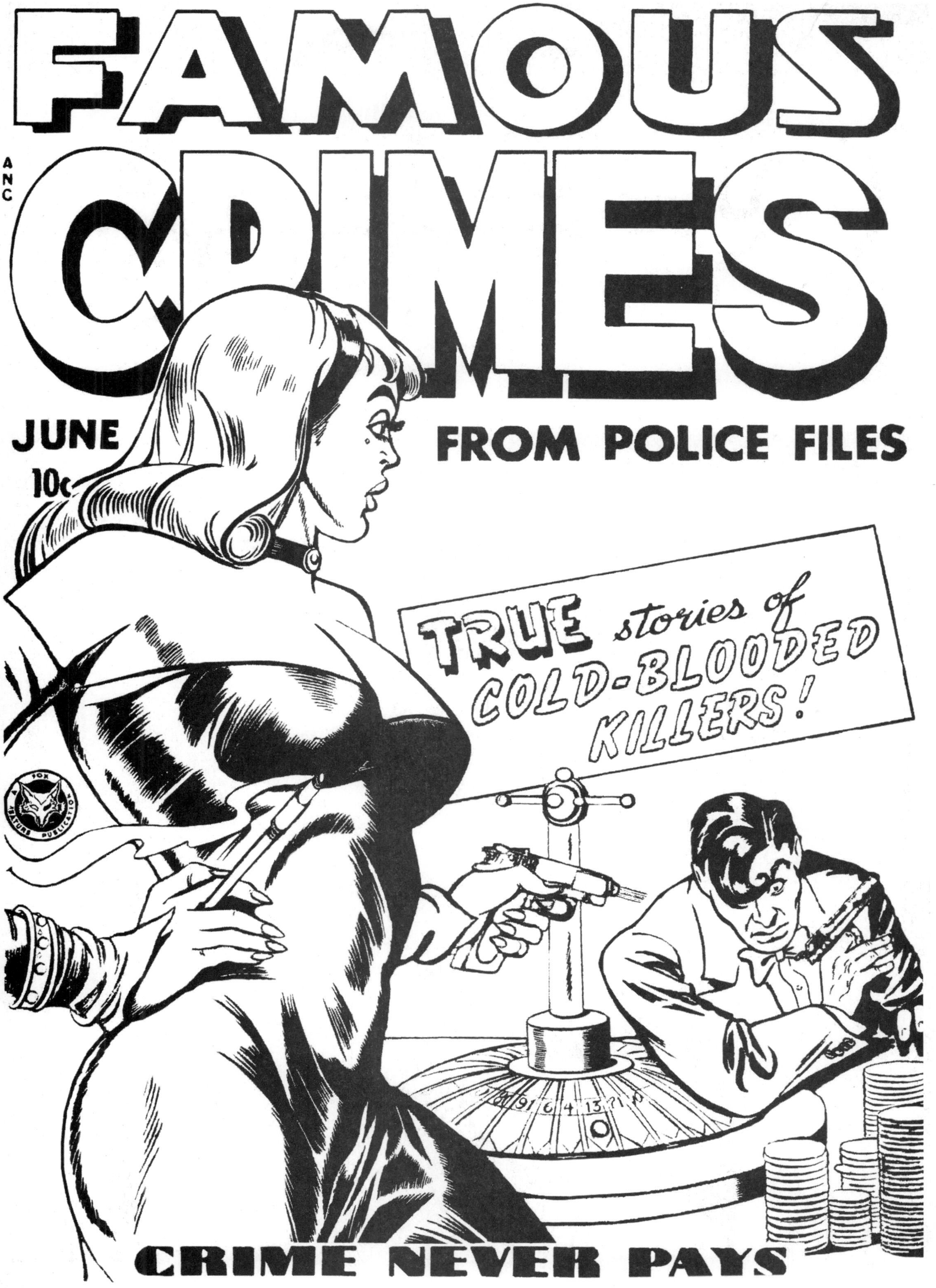

FAMOUS CRIMES

AND

JUNE
10c

FROM POLICE FILES

TRUE *stories of* COLD-BLOODED KILLERS!

CRIME NEVER PAYS

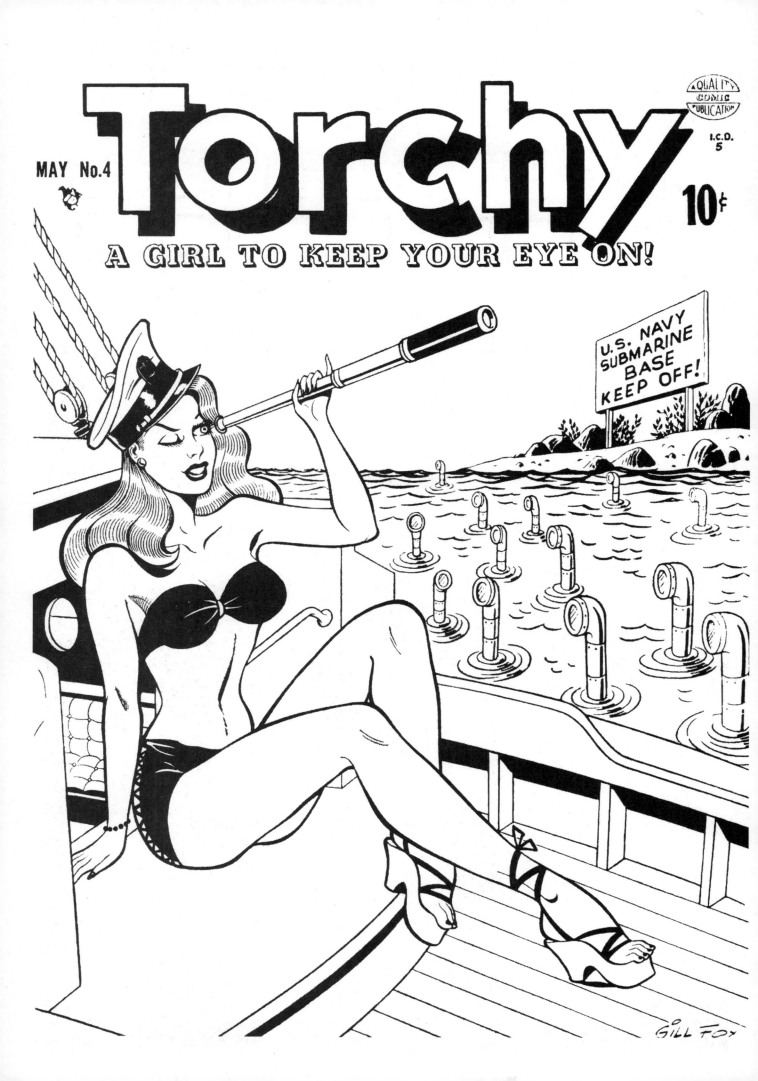

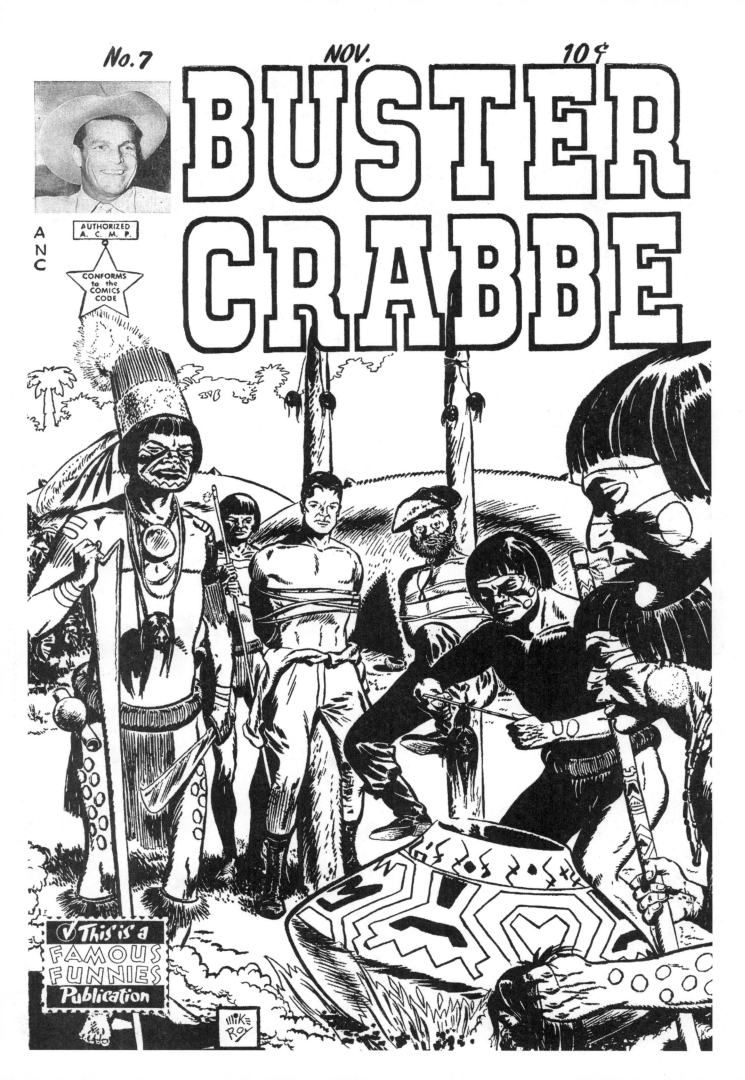

ANIMAL COMICS

10¢   **No. 4 AUGUST SEPTEMBER**

UNCLE WIGGILY'S VICTORY GARDEN

© Howard R. Garis

WEIRD ADVENTURES ON OTHER WORLDS—THE UNIVERSE OF THE FUTURE

PLANET COMICS

MAY NO. 36

10¢

GALE ALLEN
FIGHTS A SPACE RAIDER
in "COLOSSUS
OF THE
BLOOD-MOON"

also MARS
GOD OF WAR
STAR PIRATE
LOST WORLD

BOY LOVES GIRL
SEPTEMBER
NO. 38 10¢
AUTHORIZED A. C. M. P.
CONFORMS to the COMICS CODE
PDC
RITA! HAVE YOU NO SHAME?
LEV GLEASON INTEGRITY PUBLICATIONS

GHOST COMICS

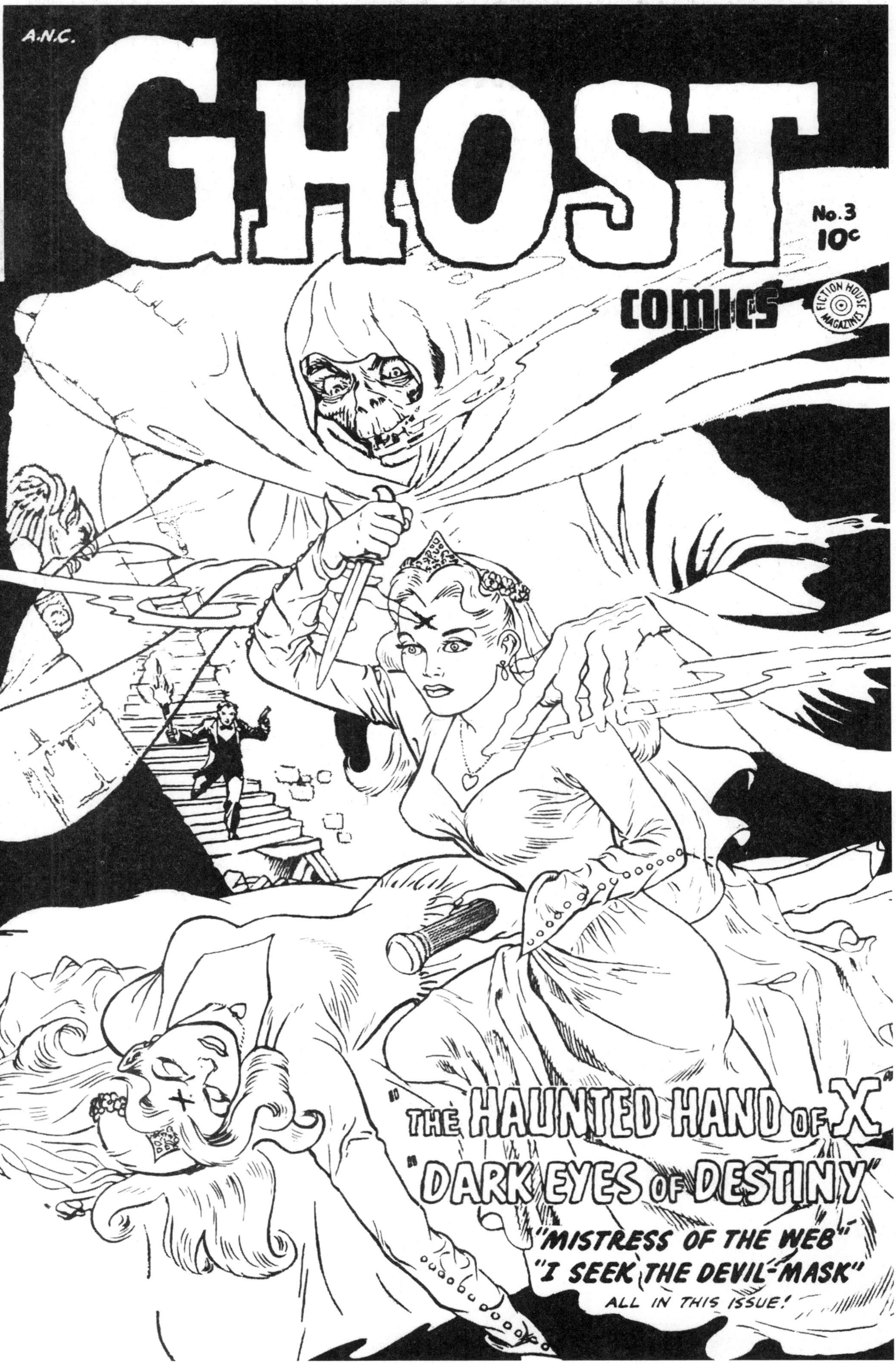

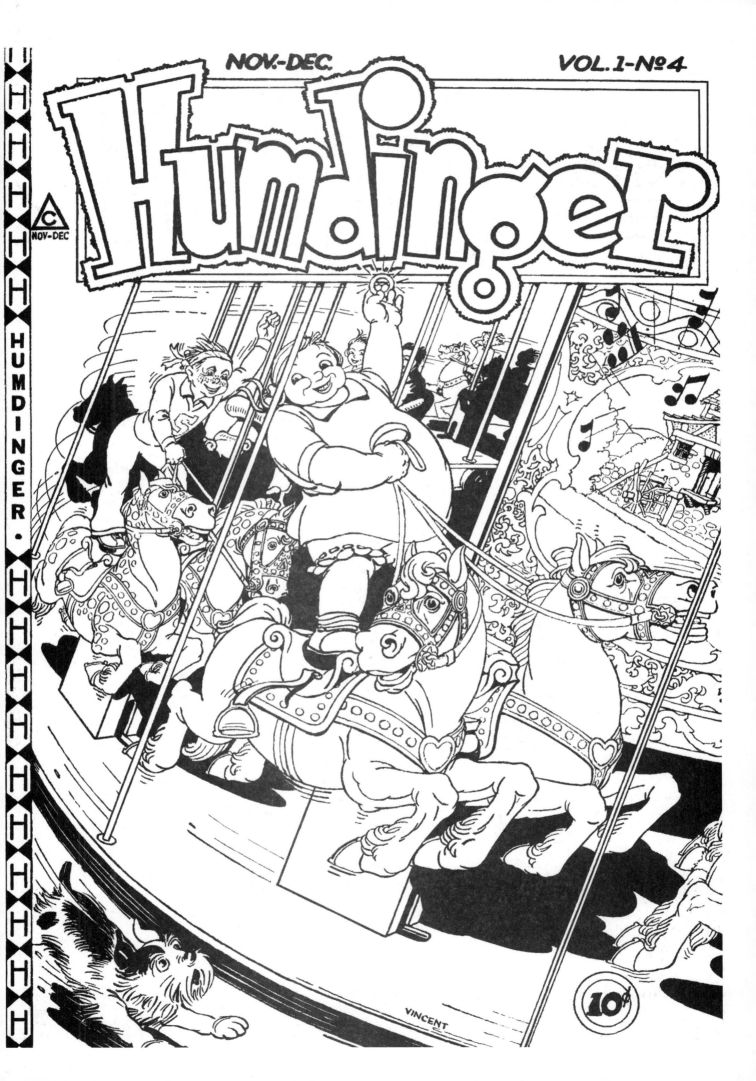

A.N.C.
JUMBO COMICS
No. 118
DEC.
10¢
SHEENA,
QUEEN OF THE JUNGLE, in
"QUEST OF THE CONGO
DWARFLINGS!"
GHOST GALLERY
AND MANY OTHERS –
FICTION HOUSE MAGAZINES
52 Pages

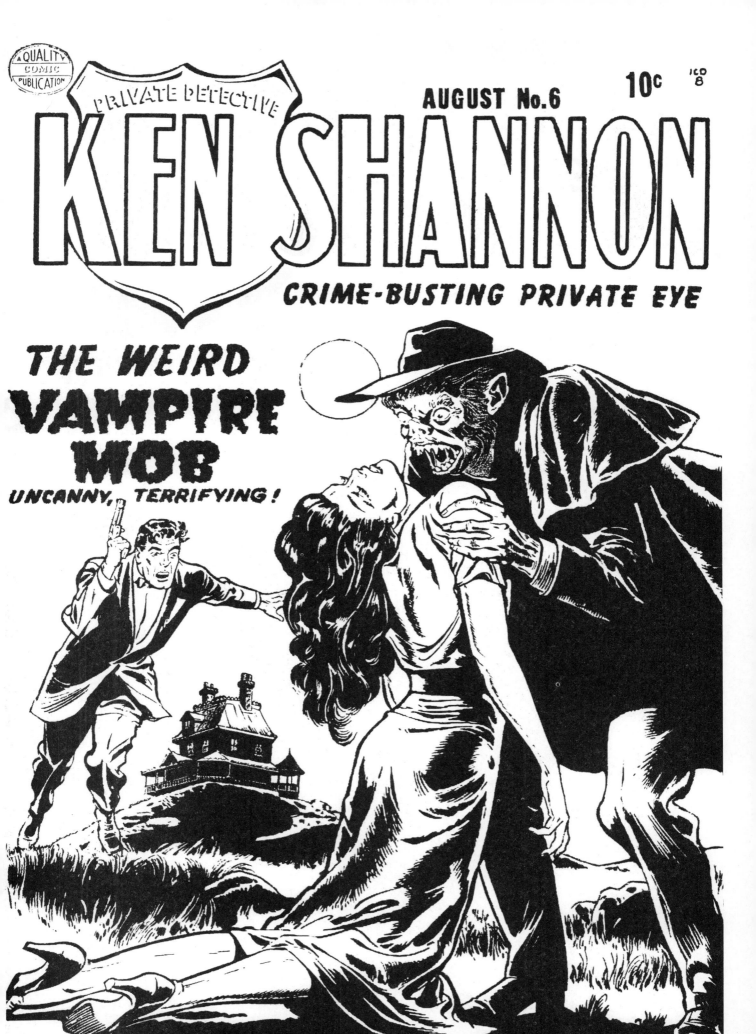

FLAMING LOVE

DECEMBER

10¢

I SAW THE SOUL SEARING PASSION IN THE EYES OF MY BELOVED AS HE TOOK THE TEMPTRESS I FEARED IN HIS ARMS---

JUNGLE PRINCESS
VOODA

A Farrell Publication

AUG
10c
K

THIS DAY WILL BECOME A JUNGLE LEGEND! EVERYTHING HAPPENED! EVEN *THE SUN BLEW AWAY!*

Also UNWARY VISITOR!

Featuring America's Fighting Nemesis of Crime

10¢

THE BLACK TERROR

NO. 13

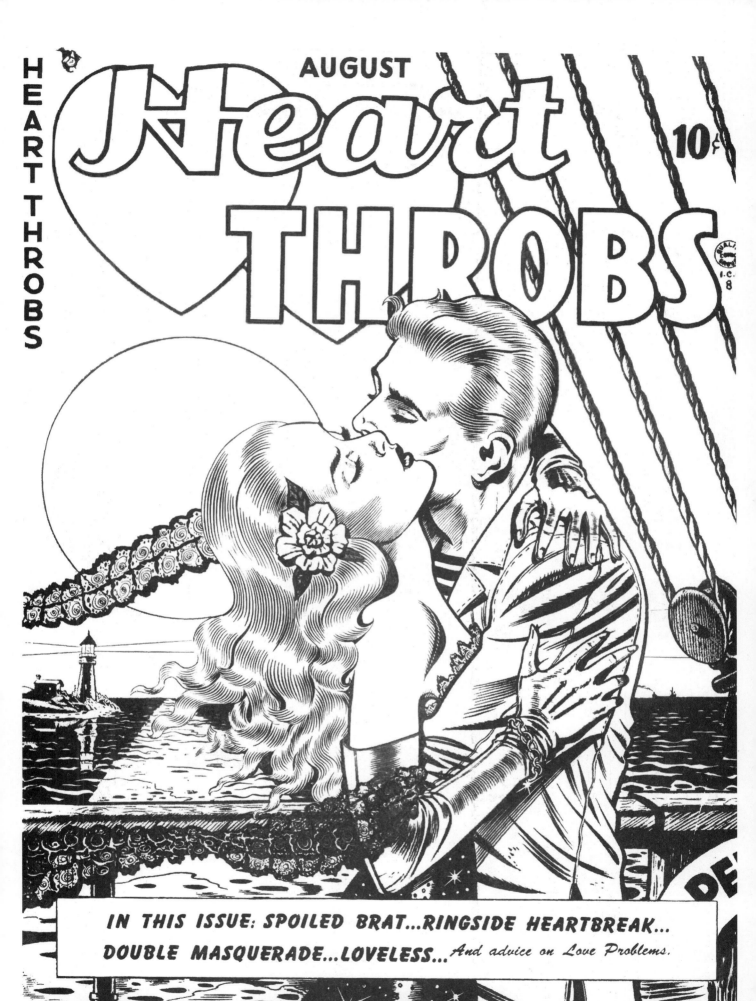

TALES of HORROR and TERROR!

HAUNTED

HAUNTED THRILLS

NOV

10c
K

A Farrell Publication

BULLETMAN.
THE FLYING DETECTIVE

No. II JAN. 13

A FAWCETT PUBLICATION
10c

BULLETMAN BATTLES THE FIENDISH FIDDLER

68 THRILL-PACKED PAGES

AN *Avon* COMIC

COW PUNCHER

NO. 2

10c

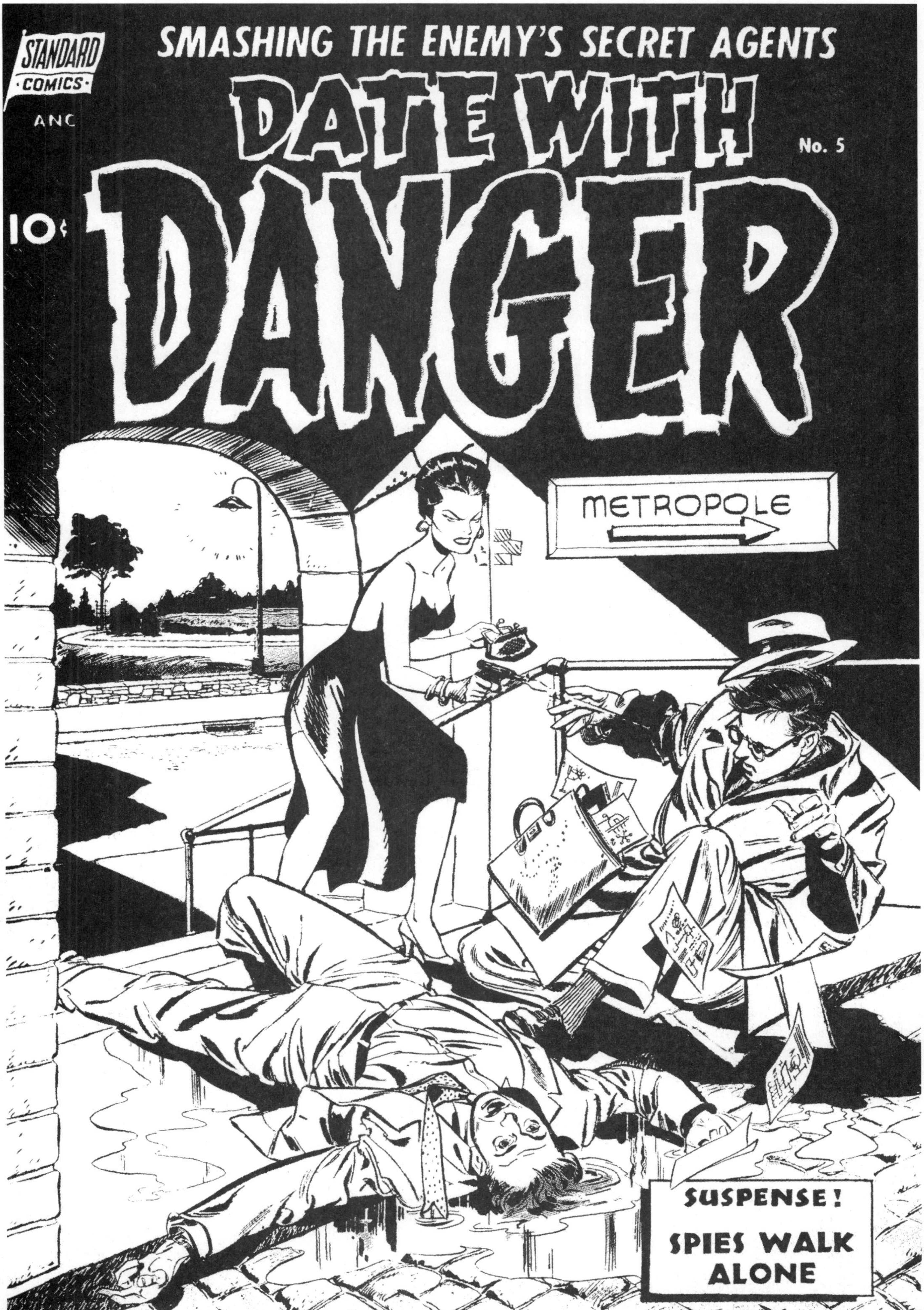

STANDARD COMICS
ANC
10¢
SMASHING THE ENEMY'S SECRET AGENTS
DATE WITH DANGER
No. 5
METROPOLE
SUSPENSE!
SPIES WALK ALONE

COWGIRL ROMANCES
COWGIRL
Romances
No. 9
10¢
FICTION HOUSE MAGAZINES
Gun-Feud Sweethearts
"Love Wears A Bogus Brand"
AND OTHER THRILLING ROMANCES OF RANCH AND RANGE.

UNUSUAL INTERPLANETARY ADVENTURES
SPACE
ACE
JUNE
10c
SPACE ACTION
SPACE ACTION
INVADERS FROM LOST GALAXY
DOUBLE MENACE ON JUPITER'S MOON
and other terrific tales

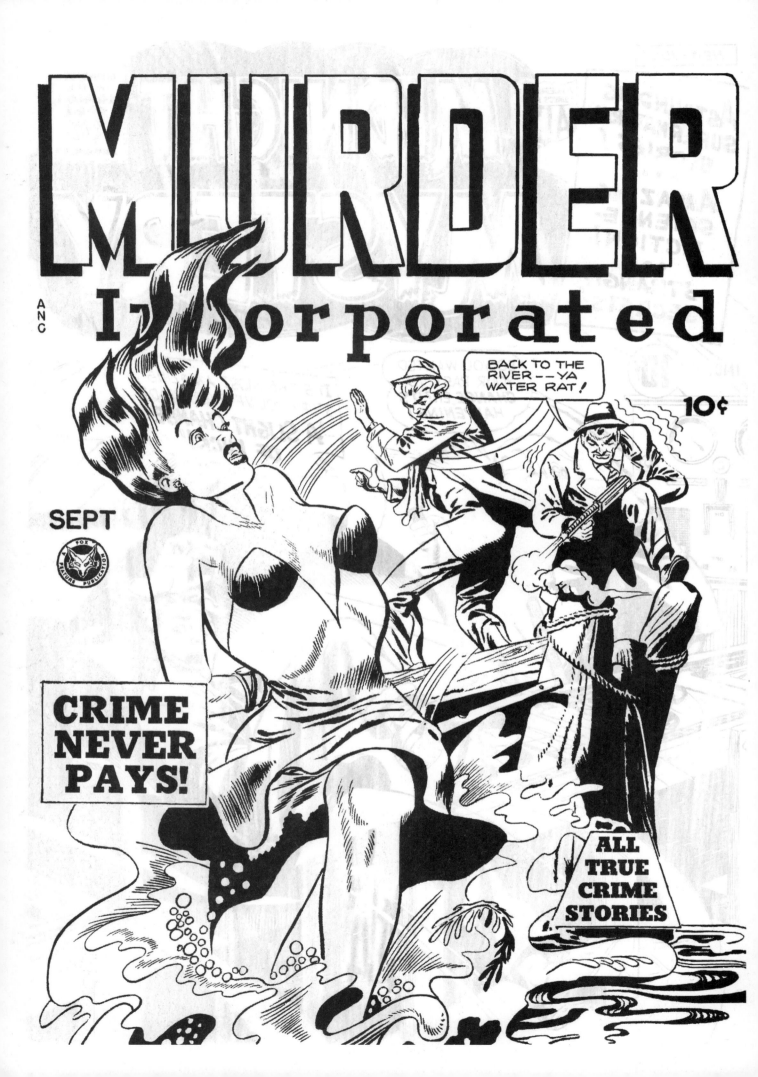

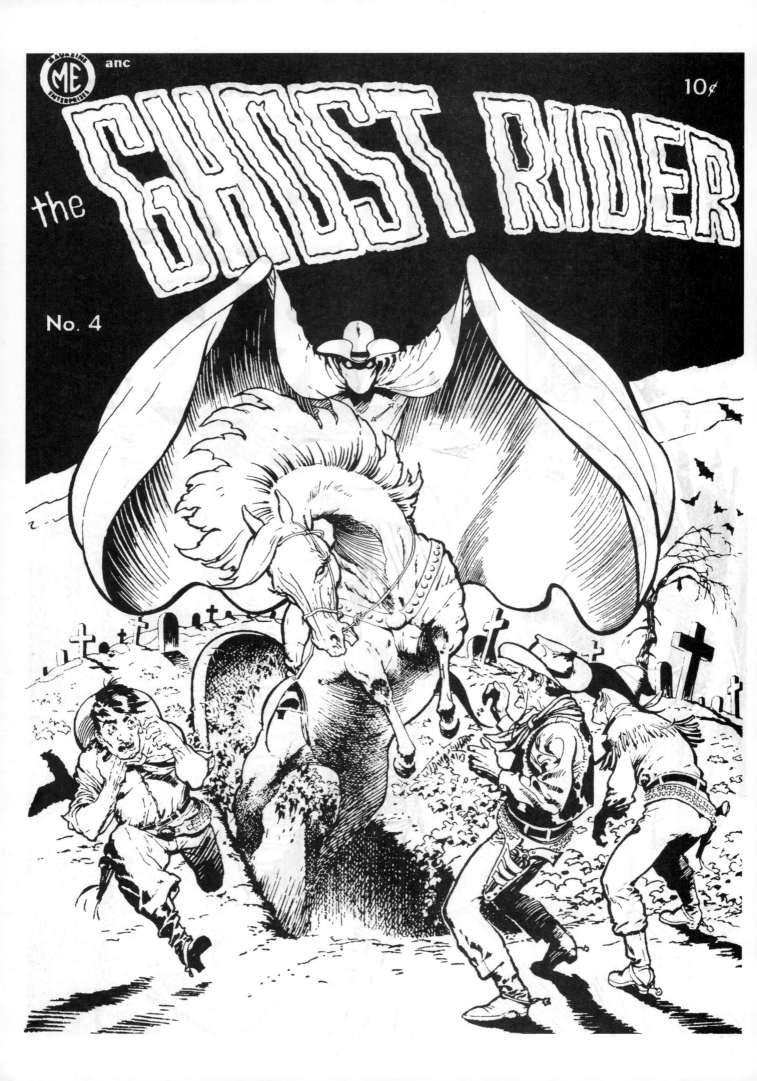

ALL NEW STORIES OF WEIRD TERRORS
A.N.C. No.2 10¢
THE MONSTER
THE MONSTER
FICTION HOUSE MAGAZINES
OUT OF THE ANCIENT OOZE IT CRAWLED—
"THE DARK ABYSMAL"
CW
"THE TIGER KISS"
"KOHNOORI'S CURSE"

MARCH   No 33   ANC

T-MAN

10c

WORLD WIDE TROUBLE-SHOOTER

A QUALITY COMIC PUBLICATION

THE RED MERMAID

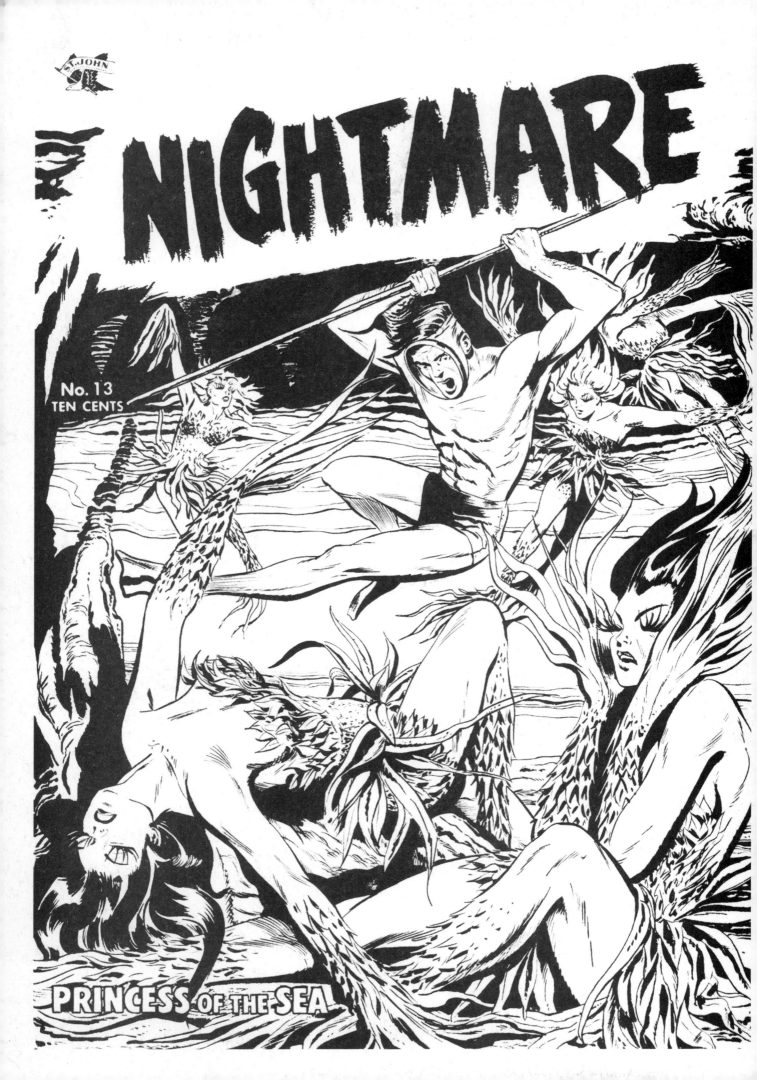